SCiENCE SPARkS

Written By

Emma Vanstone

Edited by

Jo Williams and Stuart Naylor

The **Association** *for* **Science Education**

Millgate House Education

First published 2018 by Millgate House Publishers.

Millgate House Publishers is an imprint of

Millgate House Education Ltd

A publishing arm of

The Association for Science Education

College Lane

Hatfield

AL10 9AA

Typesetting and Graphic Design by Neil Pepper and Bill Corrigan

Printed and bound in Great Britain by Cambrian Printers.

ISBN 978-0-9932486-9-6

British Library Cataloguing in Publication Data

A catalogue record for this book is available from the British Library.

FOREWORD

What's more important than the time you take with children at home, in the garden, the local park or in their amazing home-made den? We all know that our lives are fast-paced and the pressures of work can often lead to us feeling we want to spend more time with our children. Many of us seek out those opportunities that really inspire our sons, daughters, nieces, nephews, friends and grandchildren… Look no further as this colourful and rich book offers us all just that!

Science Sparks provides us with the inspiration to get involved in learning science together in an easy and engaging way. Through themed activities we can use everyday things to create extraordinary experiences that will stay with you and you children forever. Making things together, finding out why, looking, listening and talking – science discovery will come into your home or classroom and make a difference to the opportunities and choices your children have in the future.

So before you find something more important to do, take time to leaf through Science Sparks, check out what's in your cupboards and make your first strides to creating a new relationship with your children. Our world is full of rich enquiries, from sorting and hanging the washing, to cleaning the car, riding a bike, flying a kite, skidding on ice and welly-walking in puddles. Your role is to not to teach, but to learn with your children, to ask questions that you have been wanting to ask, to listen to their questions and really hear what they say… discover together!

The best thing about this book is we know it works! Emma, a mum of 4, has developed it as a result of her own experiences with her children. A truly inspirational book from a truly inspirational lady! I look forward to getting my own children engaged in such an accessible way so we can share our world together and really enjoy a new relationship with learning, with science and most importantly… with them!

Dr Lynne Bianchi

Researcher and innovator at the University of Manchester's Science & Engineering Research and Innovation Hub. She specialises in working with in-service teachers to improve the teaching and learning of primary science and engineering.

INTRODUCTION

When someone says let's do a science experiment, what's the first thing that springs to mind? Do you think of specialist equipment, laboratories and a long list of instructions to follow? Do you think of someone demonstrating something while you watch?

At Science Sparks we have a different idea. Our view is of science where children investigate, asking questions and learning through their own curiosity, using simple materials easily found around the home or classroom. My biggest piece of advice for encouraging a child to be interested in science is to let them explore. Give them the time and space to play, tinker and ask questions. If you can't answer a question, find the answer together. Investigate, research, experiment and play!

Science doesn't need to be complicated and perfectly planned. Open-ended challenges are a fantastic way for a child to learn through their own natural curiosity and problem-solving skills, learning through their own successes and mistakes. If something doesn't work, that's just part of the process. Turn it into something else, or improve on the design next time.

At Science Sparks we know how hard it can be to integrate science in the classroom, which is why our book is full of inexpensive, simple yet creative science-based learning activities. The activities can be set up for play-based learning or as more structured investigations, whichever works best in your setting. If time is limited, many activities can be completed fairly quickly, and all have easy ideas to extend the learning if more time is available, both from a science and cross-curricular perspective.

There are 40 activities, but don't be limited by our ideas. Make them bigger or smaller, messier, change the characters, and add your own twist. Each idea has been planned to improve logic, problem-solving and investigative skills whilst being visually appealing and inspiring further learning. We hope you have as much fun trying out our ideas as we had creating them.

About Emma

I have loved science for as long as I can remember. As a child, I spent a lot of time making baking soda and vinegar volcanoes with my little brother, stargazing and playing with various chemistry sets. As a teenager, science subjects were always my favourite and led to me studying Microbiology and Virology at University. After University I joined an IT graduate scheme and worked for a large bank until I had my third child. Three children under four naturally led to lots of creative, messy play, which I started to blog about, and our adventures eventually led to the creation of Science Sparks.

The activities on the website have grown along with my children, and I've been lucky enough to spend a lot of time in schools testing out our ideas, organising science afternoons and running science clubs. It's been a lot of hard work, but tremendously rewarding and inspiring to see how children respond, how one question leads to another, and how much they enjoy and benefit from science-based activities. I've lost count of the number of cards and scraps of paper that have been handed to me over the years with 'I love science' written on them, but each and every one has made me smile.

Emma Vanstone

I ♥ Science

SCiENCE SPARk

Acknowledgments

When writing the introduction I couldn't decide whether to use the words we or I and my or our when talking about Science Sparks. I decided on we and our, as Science Sparks is very much part of our family life. The children motivate me daily with their boundless enthusiasm, creativity and endless questions. They have been involved with every activity in this book and on the website, patiently helping me with photographs, thinking of ideas and designs, and generally being my inspiration. My wonderfully patient husband deserves a huge thank you for always being there to hold a camera or look after the kids so I can work, and encouraging me every step of the way.

To every person who takes the time to tweet a thank you, share a photo or just visit the website, thank you for your enthusiasm. Together we can create a generation of little scientists.

This book is dedicated in memory of a wonderful friend who shared my dream of making science fun and accessible for all. Thank you.

For Kerry xx

Incy Wincy spider

 How can you save Incy Wincy from the rain?

Incy Wincy spider climbed up the water spout,
Down came the rain and washed poor Incy out,
Out came the sunshine and dried up all the rain,
So Incy Wincy spider climbed up the spout again.

Here's what you will need

- Plastic spider
- Egg cartons or small boxes
- Aluminium foil
- Empty plastic sandwich bags
- Kitchen towel
- Newspaper
- Paper
- Sticky tape
- Water spray bottle

Here's what you can do

1 Build a structure to save Incy Wincy from the rain using just 2 different materials.

2 Your structure should be waterproof and stable enough for Incy Wincy to sit under or inside. Can you draw a plan for your structure?

3 When you build your structure, do you need to change your plan? Do you want to change anything before you test it?

4 When you're ready, place Incy Wincy spider inside your structure and spray the structure 3 times with the water sprayer.

5 Check whether Incy Wincy spider is still dry.

Science Spark

Questions to think and talk about

How did you decide which two materials to use?

What happens to the water when it lands on your structure? What can you see?

Does Incy Wincy spider get wet? What does this tell you?

How are the materials different if you spray water on them?

Is your structure still stable when it is wet?

Can you make your structure even better?

If you could add a third material, what would you choose and why?

Extra Activities

Can you make a bigger version of your structure for a really big spider? Does your structure still work?

Can you find out if your structure is weaker when it is wet?

Can you design and make a waterproof umbrella for Incy Wincy?

Links with English

Can you write a new nursery rhyme, using the words waterproof and absorbent?

Can you write a story about Incy Wincy finding shelter from the rain?

Can you write a letter to Incy Wincy's spider friends giving them instructions for how to build their own shelter?

Links with Maths

Can you find out how many sprays of water it takes for your structure to fall over?

Can you write a list of instructions with exact measurements for each material?

How would you change the measurements to make your structure twice as big?

Opportunities for learning

- Learning the names of materials.
- Learning about the properties of materials and how waterproof they are.
- Using knowledge about the materials to predict whether different materials are waterproof.
- Using key vocabulary including waterproof, transparent, flexible, absorbent, strong, weak.
- Considering similarities and differences between materials.

The cow jumped over the Moon

 How can we catapult a cow over the Moon?

Hey diddle diddle, the cat and the fiddle,
The cow jumped over the Moon.
The little dog laughed to see such fun
And the dish ran away with the spoon!

Here's what you will need

- Wooden lollysticks
- Elastic bands
- Plastic milk bottle tops
- Ping pong ball
- Pen
- Ruler
- Ball to act as the Moon

Here's what you can do

1 Our ping pong ball cow wants to jump over the Moon. Can you build a catapult to help him?

2 Use the instructions to build a simple catapult (below)

SCIENCE SPARK

Step 1

Place 6-10 lollysticks on top of each other and secure each end with a separate elastic band.

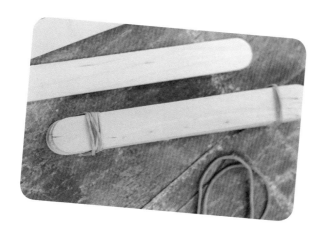

Step 2

Place two lollysticks on top of each other and secure with an elastic band at one end. Open up the sticks to make a V shape and slide the stack of sticks made in step one horizontally down the V shape until they are about two thirds of the way down. Secure another elastic band around the V shape and stack of sticks.

Step 3

Use double-sided tape or glue to attach a milk bottle top to the highest point of the catapult.

Step 4

Decorate a ping pong ball so it looks like a cow.

Place the ping pong ball cow inside the milk bottle top, push it down, release and watch your ping pong ball cow fly!

How well can you aim with your catapult?

Can you build a target to aim for?

Can you add a moon for the cow to jump over?

Science Spark

Questions to think and talk about

What happens if you push the catapult down further?

How can you make the ping pong ball travel higher or faster?

What happens if you add more lolly sticks to the centre part of the catapult?

Do you pull or push the catapult?

What do you think will happen if you use a heavier ball?

Extra Activities

Can you build a catapult using different materials?

Can you find out what difference it makes if you release the ping pong ball from a different angle?

Can you design a table or make a voice recording to collect your observations?

Can you think of any ways to improve your catapult?

What else could you use as the catapult arm? What properties should a good catapult arm have?

Links with English

Can you write a new nursery rhyme, using the words catapult and force?

Can you create a story map of your new rhyme?

Can you write instructions for a game including a catapult and a target?

Links with Maths

Create a target with different numbers on different areas. Use the catapult to aim the ping pong ball at the target. Add your scores together each time.

Can you add areas on the target, where if you hit that area your score is doubled or halved?

Can you draw a graph to show the distance your ping pong ball travels if you release it at different angles?

✓ Opportunities for learning

- Learning about the properties of materials, relating them to real life uses.

- Using key vocabulary including angle, speed, launch and distance.

- Understanding the relationship between force and motion.

- Designing and constructing the target and game.

- Measuring the distance travelled by the ping pong ball.

- How the measurements are recorded.

Making Science Fun For Kids!

Twinkle twinkle little star

> **How many stars and planets and spaceships can you catch with your magnet?**

Twinkle twinkle little star
How I wonder what you are
Up above the world so high
Like a diamond in the sky.

Here's what you will need

- Rice dyed black or dark blue
- Selection of magnetic and non-magnetic items e.g. counters, coins, paper clips
- Tweezers
- Magnet wand(s)
- Tray
- Sealable sandwich bag
- Marbles – different sizes and colours
- Stars – different sizes and colours
- Sweets or pasta shapes that resemble spaceships and rockets

Here's what you can do

1 Pour the rice into a sandwich bag so it's about half full. Add lots of food colouring and mix by squeezing the bag. When all the rice is covered, pour into a tray and leave to dry. Once it is dry, use a fork to separate any grains of rice that are stuck together.

2 Pour the rice into a large tray with your space things.

3 Use a magnet to try to catch planets, stars and spaceships. Use the tweezers if you can't catch them with a magnet.

4 Make a list of the ones you catch.

SCIENCE SPARK

Questions to think and talk about

Is it easier to pick up thick or thin things with the tweezers?

Do you have to squeeze the tweezers harder to pick up smaller things?

What happens if you put the magnet close to a metal object? Is this the same for all metals?

Can you tell if something is magnetic before you test it?

What happens if you hold two magnets together? What can you feel?

Extra Activities

How can you sort the different things in the tray?

Can you make a chart to show what you found out?

Can you investigate whether magnets always work over the same distance? Are some things attracted to a magnet from further away than others?

Can you glue a magnet to the top of a toy car and move it with another magnet?

Links with English

Can you write a letter to a friend telling them what you found out?

Can you write a list of things you can catch with a magnet and things you can't catch?

Talk about what might happen if you live on a planet where everything is magnetic.

Links with Maths

How many magnetic and non-magnetic things are there in the tray?

How many magnetic and non-magnetic things are there in the room?

What is the heaviest thing your magnet can pick up?

How many sheets of paper will your magnet attract through?

✓ Opportunities for learning

- Learning that magnets attract some materials but not others.

- Discovering how magnets attract and repel other magnets.

- Using key vocabulary such as attract, repel, magnetic, non-magnetic.

- Sorting and classifying different materials.

- Recording and displaying data.

- Considering the similarities and differences between materials.

Helping Jack and Jill

 Jack and Jill can't lift the bucket of water from the well because the windlass is broken. Can you design something to help them?

Jack and Jill went up the hill to fetch a pail of water.
Jack fell down and broke his crown and Jill came tumbling after.

Here's what you will need

- Thick string or thin rope
- Small plastic bucket with a handle
- Broom handle
- Ribbon spool that fits over a cane or dowel
- Small objects to lift (you could use bags of sand)

Here's what you can do

1 Attach a small bucket onto the end of a piece of string or rope. Add enough weight to the bucket so it is hard to lift by hand.

2 Attach the string to the bucket and pull up using the rope.

3 Lift it again, this time passing the string over a broom handle and pulling on the string.

4 Lift it again, this time passing the string over a ribbon spool on a cane and pulling on the string.

SCIENCE SPARK

Questions to think and talk about

When is it easiest to lift the bucket?

How long does the string/rope need to be?

How do people get water from a well without having to pull too hard?

Links with English

People using pulleys to lift heavy loads need to be careful. Can you create a list of safety rules for them to follow?

Can you write a story about a family that always gets water from a well, but now the well has dried up?

Links with Maths

Weigh different items for your bucket and sort them so you have three loads of different weights to lift. How long does it take to lift each load using the roller (remember the same person should lift each time to make it fair).

Place your items in order of how much they weigh, then in order of size. Does the order change much?

Extra Activities

Find out whether using thicker or thinner string makes any difference.

Find out whether using smooth or rough string or rope makes any difference.

Can you find a design for a double pulley on the internet? Can you make one? Is it easier or harder to lift the bucket?

Can you build a model of a lift using a pulley system and cardboard boxes?

✓ Opportunities for learning

- Understanding that a roller reduces friction.
- Measuring and recording weights.
- Comparing and ordering objects in different ways.
- Understanding that pulley systems are more efficient at raising loads than rollers.

A zip wire for Tinkerbell

 Tinkerbell has run out of pixie dust. Can you build a zip wire and harness to rescue her from Captain Hook?

Here's what you will need

- String or strong fishing line
- Tinkerbell fairy figure
- Drinking straw, cut into thirds
- Pipe cleaners
- Timer
- Paper and pencil

Here's what you can do

1 You need to find something to attach your zip wire to. If you are outside, two trees should work well.

2 Tie one end of your string as high as you can reach around one tree. Slide a piece of a drinking straw onto the string. The straw will form part of Tinkerbell's harness.

3 Then tie the other end of the string around the base of another tree.

4 Find a way to attach Tinkerbell to the zip wire using the straw and pipe cleaner. You could make a simple harness using a pipe cleaner, with one end looped around the zip wire and one around Tinkerbell.

5 Let Tinkerbell slide down the zip wire. Use a timer to measure how long she takes to reach the bottom.

Science Spark

Questions to think and talk about

What do you think will happen if you push Tinkerbell down the zip wire?

What do you think will happen if you make the zip wire longer?

What do you think will happen if you make the zip wire steeper?

What do you think will happen if you use a heavier figure?

Does changing the harness affect how quickly Tinkerbell travels?

Extra Activities

See if you can find a way to make Tinkerbell go faster or slower down the zip wire.

Try comparing a zip wire made from rough string with one made from smooth string. Try comparing one made from thick string with one made from thin string.

Links with English

Talk about how Tinkerbell would feel if she was pushed down the zip wire.

What happens when Tinkerbell reaches the bottom? Can you write another paragraph for your story?

Can you write a story about what Tinkerbell did when she ran out of pixie dust?

Links with Maths

How long is your zip wire? Can you find three different ways to measure it?

Can you record the time it takes for Tinkerbell to reach the bottom of the zip wire using three different slopes? Write the times in order, starting with the shortest time.

Opportunities for learning

- Working scientifically by making observations, performing simple tests, gathering and recording data, solving problems.

- Carrying out comparative tests; beginning to understand how to make a test fair by only changing one variable.

- Investigating and understanding that changing the incline or changing the material of a zip wire changes how fast Tinkerbell travels.

- Recognising friction as a force that slows an object down.

- Using key vocabulary including speed, distance, incline, slope, friction.

Activity 6

A secret message for Hansel and Gretel

 The birds have eaten Hansel's breadcrumbs. Can you find another way for him to leave a message for his Dad?

Here's what you will need

- White paper or card
- Lemon or lemon juice
- White crayon
- Paint brushes
- Heat source
- Watercolour paint

Here's what you can do

Write a secret message to Hansel and Gretel's Dad so he can find them more easily in the forest.

1 **Crayon message**

Write a message on a piece of white paper or card using a white crayon. You will need to press down quite hard. Use watercolour paints to paint over the message on the paper.

2 **Lemon juice message**

Squeeze the juice from a lemon into a container. Dip a paintbrush into the lemon juice and use it to write a message. Ask an adult to place the paper in an oven for a few minutes or place under a hairdryer.

SciENCE SPark

Questions to think and talk about

Which message is easiest to read?

Which message is most invisible before you reveal it?

Why is white crayon good for writing secret messages?

If you need to send a secret message, which type of secret writing would you use? Why would you choose this one?

Links with English

Can you write a new version of Hansel and Gretel where the children leave a message for their Dad using one of the methods above?

Can you write a set of instructions so a friend knows how to reveal your secret message.

Links with Maths

Can you time how long it takes each message to show up?

Extra Activities

Can you write a longer message in your secret writing?

Can you reveal the white crayon message by crayoning over it lightly with a different colour crayon instead of using watercolour paints?

Can you think of any other ways to send a secret message?

Opportunities for learning

- Observing simple irreversible chemical reactions.
- Observing how substances change when exposed to heat.
- Using key vocabulary including change, visible, invisible.
- Considering similarities and difference between substances.
- Reimagining the story of Hansel and Gretel.

Making Science Fun For Kids!

A pirate boat for Captain Hook

 Captain Hook needs a new pirate boat to get to shore. Can you build one for him?

Here's what you will need

- Paper or card
- Elastic bands
- Corks
- Lolly sticks
- Pirate decorations
- Washing up sponges
- Plasticine
- Glue and sellotape
- Double-sided tape
- Pens and scissors
- Water tray for testing

Here's what you can do

Use the materials to build a new boat for Captain Hook. Your boat must float on its own. Test it in a sink or water tray. Put a pirate figure on the boat. Does it still float?

1 **Cork boat**
   Place three corks in a row and wrap an elastic band around them to hold them together. Cut out a sail shape from paper or cardboard and attach it to a lolly stick using sellotape. Push the lolly stick into the centre cork to make a sail.

2 **Sponge boat**
   Get a piece of sponge that is a good size for a boat. You might want to cut it into a boat shape with scissors. Cut out a sail shape from paper or cardboard and attach it to a lolly stick using sellotape. Push the lolly stick into the centre of the sponge to make a sail.

3 **Lolly stick raft**
   Place 8 lolly sticks together in a row. Attach double-sided tape to two more lolly sticks and stick these to your 8 lolly sticks so they lie in the opposite direction.

Do this on both sides of your raft.

SCiENCE SPARk

Questions to think and talk about

Which boat can hold the most weight before it sinks?

Does the sponge boat still float when it is wet?

Does a small lolly stick raft hold more weight before sinking than a bigger raft? Does placing an object on each corner of the raft work better than placing them all in the centre?

How can you make your boat more buoyant?

Extra Activities

Can you build a boat that will hold even more weight without sinking?

What's the smallest boat you can build that will float?

Can you use a straw to blow waves across the water? Does your boat move faster the harder you blow?

Is it easier to move a small raft or big raft with wind from a straw?

Links with English

Can you write a story about Captain Hook and his new boat? Does it survive the trip to shore or does he have to fix things that go wrong?

Can you create a code so Captain Hook can leave a message for his crew mates no one else will understand?

Links with Maths

Can you time how long it takes to race your boat across the water using a straw to blow the boat?

Can you find out how much extra weight each boat can hold before sinking?

Can you draw a map for the pirates, giving them directions to the shore?

✓ Opportunities for learning

- Observing whether different objects sink or float.

- Learning how different materials can be used to make a boat more buoyant.

- Using key vocabulary including sink, float, heavy, light, strong, buoyant.

- Considering similarities and differences between materials.

- Measuring size, weight, distance.

- Considering how the force from the air blown down the straw affects the speed the boat travels.

A bed for Goldilocks

 Goldilocks has broken the bears' chair, but she doesn't want to break their beds as well. Can you build her a strong bed?

Here's what you will need

- Cardboard boxes, assorted sizes and thicknesses
- Elastic bands, variety of sizes
- Corks
- Lolly sticks
- Cardboard tubes
- Washing up sponges
- Bits of bubble wrap
- Scraps of different fabrics
- Glue and sellotape
- Double-sided tape

Here's what you can do

Use the materials to build a bed for Goldilocks.

The bed needs to have four legs and be comfortable for Goldilocks to sleep in.

It needs to be strong. You can test your bed with a 500g bag of sugar or flour.

Science Spark

Questions to think and talk about

What can you do to make the bed strong?

What can you do to make the bed comfortable?

Do you think a bed will work if it has three legs? What do you think might be a problem with a three-legged bed?

Extra Activities

Can you build bunk beds so Goldilocks can have a friend to stay? Are bunk beds as strong as a single bed?

Can you build a bed that will hold twice as much weight?

Links with English

Can you write a story describing what happens when Goldilocks moves in with the three bears? How do the bears feel about their new house guest?

Can you write a set of instructions for how to build the bed?

Can you write a letter from Goldilocks to her parents telling them about her new adventure?

Links with Maths

What's is the maximum amount of weight your bed can hold without collapsing?

Does your bed hold more weight if you spread it around or if you place it all in the centre?

✓ Opportunities for learning

- Learning about the properties of materials and relating them to real life uses.
- Using key vocabulary including strong, weak, comfortable, collapse.
- Designing and constructing a bed.
- Investigating whether the bed can hold more weight if it is distributed evenly.

Activity 9

Playing with plants

> How do we know what parts a plant has? How do we know what we are eating?
>
> Let's find out!

Here's what you will need

- A4 thin card, different colours
- Different plants, including the roots – e.g. dandelions, bluebells, daffodils, tulips
- Materials such as felt, coloured cellophane, fabrics, straws, pipe cleaners, string, etc.
- A range of edible plants, such as carrots, leeks, turnips, beetroot, cress, spinach, lettuce, courgettes, fennel, parsnips
- Paper and coloured pencils
- Sellotape and/or glue

Here's what you can do

1 Take a plant apart. Stick all the bits separately on card so it looks like the plant has exploded.

2 Find out what the different bits of the plant are called and what they do. Stick labels on your exploded picture. Use one colour label for what the parts are called and a different colour label for what the parts do.

3 Make your own plant from different materials (e.g. felt, coloured card, coloured cellophane, fabrics, straws, pipe cleaners, string, etc). Create labels for your plant.

4 Get some different plants that we eat from a shop – e.g. carrots, leeks, turnips, beetroot, cress, spinach, lettuce, courgettes, fennel, parsnips . . . See if you can decide which bits of these plants are the bits that we eat. Make yourself a tasty salad!

SCiENCE SPARK

Questions to think and talk about

Most people buy their food from shops. What do you think people did before there were any shops?

Lots of plants are good to eat. Why do you think some plants store food that we can eat?

Where do you think plants will grow well? What makes you think this?

Extra Activities

Closely observe 3 or 4 different types of plants. Make a compare and contrast table to show what's the same about the plants and what's different about them.

Create your own superfood plant. Get the bits that we eat from different plants and stick them together to make a fantastic food plant. What will you call your plant?

Links with English

Can you write a care label for a plant to make sure it gets looked after properly?

Can you write a story about a bee travelling from flower to flower? Which flowers does your bee go to? Does the bee like particular colours and smells?

Links with Maths

Do different types of flowers have different numbers of petals?

Make a collection of flowers with different numbers of petals. Put them in a table to show how many petals they have. What is the smallest number of petals you can find on a plant? What is the biggest number?

✓ Opportunities for learning

- Finding out about the different parts of a plant and their functions.
- Observing different edible plants and analysing their parts.
- Comparing and contrasting different plants.

Autumn treasure stick

> How many different autumn leaves and seeds can you find to stick on your treasure stick? Do you know which type of tree they came from?

Here's what you will need

- A large stick
- Double-sided tape
- Leaves, acorns, small pinecones, conkers (horse chestnuts), seeds

Here's what you can do

1 Attach double-sided tape to your stick and remove the covering.
2 Go for a walk and stick beautifully-coloured leaves, seeds and other natural items to your stick as you go.

SCIENCE SPARK

Questions to think and talk about

Can you match the leaves and seeds to the type of tree they dropped from?

Why do you think some seeds are inside a spiky case?

Did you find any items you can eat on your walk? Autumn is a great time of year to forage for blackberries and sweet chestnuts.

Extra Activities

Can you make a picture using your leaves?

Try making a model from your collected items. How about a pinecone mouse, or a mini person using sticks for arms, acorns for legs and a pinecone body?

Do you have a large leaf that would make a great sail for a stick raft?

Leave your pinecones on a windowsill outside and observe them for a few days. You should notice that they close up when the weather is wet, to protect the seeds inside from the rain.

Links with English

Imagine you're a squirrel and need to collect nuts and seeds to survive winter. Write about how you think the squirrel might feel about the changing seasons. Think about how the trees might have changed and where might be a good place to hide your food.

Can you write a squirrel survival guide?

Links with Maths

How many different colours can you see in your leaves? Can you sort and then order them from lightest to darkest?

Can you make a symmetrical piece of art using your collected items?

Imagine you're a squirrel again. Draw a map of the wood you live in and mark areas where you have hidden seeds. Can you write directions from one area to another for a squirrel friend to follow?

 Opportunities for learning

- Observing changes across seasons.

- Describing weather associated with different seasons.

- Identifying evergreen and deciduous trees.

- Identifying nuts and seeds and matching them to the trees they come from.

Cress monster!

Can you choose materials to make a friendly monster and find a way to make grass hair grow from its head?

Here's what you will need

- Egg cartons
- Washing up sponges
- Egg shells
- Empty yoghurt containers
- Lower section of a small water bottle
- Cotton wool
- Old tights
- Cress seeds
- Water spayer
- Stick-on eyes

Here's what you can do

Create a friendly monster using any of the materials above. Think about where the cress hair will grow. Remember the monster needs to be able to stand up on its own.

1 If you are using sponges, you can sprinkle cress seeds on the top and spray with water.

2 If you are using egg shells, yoghurt pots, water bottles or egg cartons, you can place a bit of cotton wool inside the container and sprinkle it with seeds, then spray with water.

3 Another idea is to sprinkle cress seeds into the end of one leg of old tights and stuff with cotton wool. Tie off the end and use this as your monster's face.

4 Don't forget to spray your monster at least once each day so that the seeds grow into hair.

SCiENCE SPAR[

Questions to think and talk about

What will the cress monster need to grow?

Where should you put your cress monster for the hair to grow as fast as possible?

Where could you put the cress monster if you want the hair to be yellow?

Links with English

Can you write a letter to your monster telling it how to make its hair grow?

Can you write a fantasy story about how your cress monster is terrified of sheep?

Links with Maths

Can you keep a record of how many days it takes your monster's hair to grow, and then measure it every two days?

How much hair will you cut off when you give your monster a haircut?

Extra Activities

See if you can grow grass hair, or a mixture of cress and grass hair.

Try keeping your monster in the dark and find out whether the cress still grows.

Try keeping your monster in the fridge and find out what happens.

Opportunities for learning

- Investigating what conditions plants need to grow.
- Recognising roots, stems and leaves.
- Considering how the environment in which a plant grows can affect its health and growth.
- Exploring different materials and how to use them for a purpose.

Great greenhouses

 You want to grow some herbs but the weather has turned very cold. How can you protect your young plants?

Here's what you will need

- Empty CD cases
- Empty, clean plastic bottles
- Plastic containers
- Craft sticks
- Sellotape
- Glue
- Glass jars
- Plastic cups
- Seedlings in pots – e.g. parsley, sage, thyme, basil

Here's what you can do

1 Design and build a mini-greenhouse to protect your seedlings.

2 When you draw a design for your greenhouse, think about the properties the materials you use should have. Your greenhouse needs to let air and sunlight in and keep rain and wind out.

3 You can make a simple tiny greenhouse using a transparent plastic bottle, container or jar. You can make a bigger structure using CD cases or plastic bottles taped together.

SCIENCE SPAR

Questions to think and talk about

Greenhouses are great for growing plants where there isn't much space. How big do you want your greenhouse to be?

Where should you place your greenhouse? Think about the conditions a plant needs to grow.

How could you improve the design for your greenhouse? Can you find a way to let air in but keep insects out?

Extra Activities

Can you make some labels for your plants using natural materials?

Try growing a new plant from a fruit or vegetable. Try burying a tomato slice in a plant pot or placing a carrot top in water. Plant the tops in soil when they sprout shoots. How many plants can you grow from one fruit or vegetable?

Can you use a plastic bottle and ruler to make a simple rain gauge?

Links with English

Imagine you could grow a new fruit or vegetable? What would it look, feel, smell and taste like?

Write a list of the things plants needs to grow successfully and things that people need to survive. How are they similar and how are they different?

Links with Maths

Measure and record the height of your seedlings each day. Can you create a graph or table to record your results?

Have a bean race with your friends. Each of you plants a bean in a mini-greenhouse. When the beans grow into seedlings, plant them outside in a row and record the height of each every week. Which bean grows fastest?

Opportunities for learning

- Understanding the conditions needed for seeds to grow into healthy plants.

- Observing and describing how seeds grow into plants and how an environment can be manipulated to provide optimal conditions for growth.

- Measuring and recording data.

Wonderful windmills

 You live on a windy hill and would like to use the wind to make electricity. Can you design a windmill that turns in the wind?

Here's what you will need

- Cylindrical container
- Sellotape and glue
- Scissors
- Cardboard
- 4 craft sticks
- Length of dowel
- Stickers or marker pens
- Small circle of card
- Drinking straw
- Timer

Here's what you can do

1 Attach 4 craft sticks evenly around the small circle of card.

2 Ask an adult to make a hole in the round container that just fits the dowel.

3 Place the dowel in the hole and attach the small circle of card. Check that it spins. You might need to adjust the length of the dowel so that it is supported.

4 Use stickers or marker pens to decorate your windmill.

Make the windmill blades spin using your hands. Now try blowing with your mouth or down a straw, or fanning it with a big piece of card.

Try timing how long the blades spin when you blow lightly and then more forcefully.

SCiENCE SPARk

Questions to think and talk about

How did you decide how big to make the blades? Do you think they should all be the same size? Does it make any difference if they are different sizes?

Can you make the windmill blades spin faster? What weather conditions would you need for the windmill blades to spin well outside?

Why do you think windmills can only be used successfully in certain areas?

Extra Activities

Try using different materials for the blades and see if this makes a difference.

Can you make a simple pinwheel windmill?

Where might be a good place to put this outside so it spins well?

What can you find out about how wind is used to make electricity in this country? Which countries get most electricity from the wind?

Links with English

Imagine you are standing in front of a large wind farm where all the windmills are spinning very quickly. How does it make you feel? What do you think you will be able to hear?

Imagine a world with no electricity. How do you think your life would be different? Can you write about three things that would be harder to do with no electricity?

Links with Maths

Can you record how long the windmill takes to stop spinning after you blow it? Try using different blade materials and record your results in a table.

How does the area of the blade change if you make it twice the size? What difference do you think this will make to how quickly the windmill turns?

Opportunities for learning

- Problem-solving in constructing a working model.

- Understanding the effect of air resistance on the windmill blades.

- Understanding that wind power is a renewable source of energy.

It's too loud!

 Your friend is learning to play the drums and is VERY loud. Can you find a way to reduce the noise level from her bedroom?

▶ Here's what you will need

- Cardboard box with lid (e.g. a shoebox)
- Sellotape and scissors
- Something to make a noise, such as a small radio or buzzer
- Bubble wrap
- Aluminium foil
- Foam and felt sheets
- Cotton wool
- Sponge
- Egg boxes
- Newspaper

Here's what you can do

1 Check that the cardboard box closes tightly.

2 Place a buzzer or radio inside the box and note how loud the sound is.

3 Choose three of the materials that you think will muffle the noise well.

4 Line the box with one of the materials, place the buzzer/radio inside, close the lid and note how loud the sound is.

5 Repeat for your two other materials.

Science Spark

Questions to think and talk about

Can you tell how loud the sound is just by listening?

Can you find a way to measure how loud the sound is?

How did you choose the three materials to test? Which is best?

Can you think of any ways you could improve your sound test?

What might very loud sounds do to your ears?

Links with English

Can you create a list of different ways to protect your ears from loud noises?

Links with Maths

Find out how many steps you take away from the cardboard box before you can't hear the sound. Can you display your results in a table or graph?

How far away can you hear a pin drop?

Extra Activities

What happens if you use more than one layer of each material? Does it affect the sound?

What happens if you use a bigger or smaller box? Does the size of box affect the sound?

Can you use what you have learnt to make a pair of ear muffs to protect your ears from loud noises?

SAFETY: do not put anything inside your ear!

✓ Opportunities for learning

- Understanding that sound travels through the air and can be absorbed by different materials.

- Understanding that some materials are better at absorbing sound than others.

- Deciding how to set up a fair test investigation.

Three little pig houses

 The three little pigs' houses have all fallen down. Can you rebuild them before the Big Bad Wolf comes?

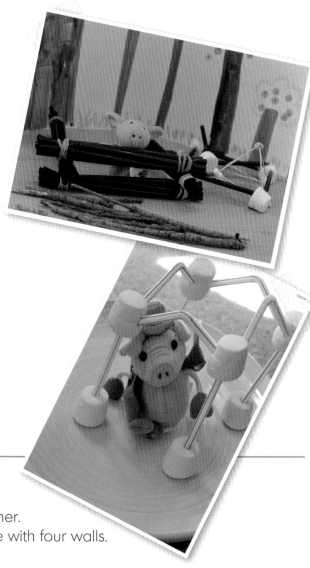

Here's what you will need

- Sticks - e.g. lolly sticks
- Craft sticks
- Drinking straws - plastic and paper
- Elastic bands
- Marshmallows or plasticine/ playdough
- Sugar cubes
- Squeezy bottle or small fan to use as wind

Here's what you can do

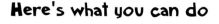

1 **Straw House**
   Put straws in bundles of 5.
   Use elastic bands to hold the straws together.
   Use the bundles of straws to make a house with four walls.
   Use single straws to make the roof.

2 **Stick House**
   Arrange sticks to make four walls of a stick house.
   Use plasticine or marshmallows at the corners to hold the sticks in position.
   Use more sticks to make the roof.

3 **Brick House**
   Put sugar cubes in lines to make the walls of a house.
   Balance some straws across the walls, then put sugar cubes on the straws to make the roof.

Use a small fan or squeezy bottle to blow air on your houses. Do your houses blow over? Are they strong enough to stay upright?

SCIENCE SPARK

Questions to think and talk about

Which materials are easiest to build with?

What shape house is easiest to build?

Which house is the strongest when the wind blows?

What happens if you shake your houses? Is the same one still strongest?

Links with English

Can you write a new version of The Three Little Pigs where the wolf can't blow down any of the houses?

Can you create a poster warning the wolf to stay away?

Links with Maths

How many puffs of air does it take before the houses fall down?

How many times can you shake each house before it falls down?

Can you make your houses stronger so they stand up for a minute?

Extra Activities

Do you think your houses will be waterproof? Can you test to see if the houses are waterproof by spraying them with water?

Can you test different natural roof materials to see if they are waterproof?

What does water look like on the surface of a waterproof material?

Opportunities for learning

- Evaluating materials for suitability for a task.

- Setting up a suitable scientific test.

- Using fine motor skills and manipulating materials.

- Using suitable materials for strength or to make the house waterproof.

- Observing that water remains on the surface of a waterproof material and is absorbed by a non-waterproof material.

- Using appropriate language, including strong, weak, waterproof, absorbent.

Lifeguard towers

> You've been asked to help keep holidaymakers safe on the beach. The first thing you need to do is build a tower to give you a better view of swimmers in the sea. It needs to be stable and have a platform at the top.

Here's what you will need

- Masking tape and sellotape
- Drinking straws
- Toothpicks
- Craft sticks and lengths of dowel
- Pegs
- Blocks
- Play dough
- Cardboard tubes
- Cardboard

Here's what you can do

1 Design and construct a lifeguard tower using a selection of materials. Remember it must stand up and be able to support a platform.

SCIENCE SPARk

Questions to think and talk about

What properties should a lifeguard tower have?

What features would make the lifeguard more comfortable? Hint – some shade from the Sun, somewhere to store water?

How could you make your tower stronger?

What shape is your tower? Why did you choose that shape?

How would you change your design?

Extra Activities

Can you make your tower a little taller?

Can you investigate to find out how much weight the platform on your tower can hold without collapsing?

Try making shapes using craft sticks and clips or K'nex. Investigate what happens when you try to rotate the sticks and whether some shapes are stronger than others.

Links with English

Can you write a list of equipment a lifeguard might need when sat at the top of the tower?

How do you think people can keep themselves safe on the beach? Can you write a list of rules people should follow?

Links with Maths

Can you record how much weight your tower can hold without collapsing? You could build one tower with a square framework and one with a triangle framework and investigate which can hold the most weight.

How many shapes can you make with craft sticks? Can you turn one shape into another by adding extra sticks?

Opportunities for learning

- Recognising 2D and 3D shapes.
- Understanding the role of a lifeguard and the dangers of the sea.
- Understanding that some shapes are stronger than others.
- Thinking about how to create a fair investigation.
- Designing, planning and following instructions creatively.

Moving with magnets

 Can you find a way to make a car or boat move without touching it?

Here's what you will need

- Small bar magnets
- Magnet wand or large magnet
- Small toy cars or boats
- Strong glue dots
- Container of water or plastic guttering (for boats)
- Thick cardboard to make a ramp (optional)

Here's what you can do

1 Place a sticky glue dot onto the top of a small car or boat.

2 Press a small bar magnet hard into the glue dot.

3 Place the car onto a flat surface or the boat onto water and try to get it to move using the magnet wand.

SCIENCE SPARK

Questions to think and talk about

Does it matter which part of the magnet wand or large magnet you use to move the car or boat?

What does the N and S on a magnet mean?

How does it feel if you place the north pole of one magnet next to the north pole of another magnet? Can you make them touch each other?

Can you find a way to make the car or boat move backwards?

Extra Activities

Can you make a ramp for your car using a thick sheet of cardboard? Can you get the car to move up the ramp using the magnet?

Ask a friend to blow waves over the surface of the water with a straw. Can you use the magnet to move the boat through the waves safely? Is it harder to move the boat when the water is not still?

Have a race with a friend. Who can get their car or boat to the finish line first?

Links with English

Can you write a story about a child who loses something containing iron and uses a magnet to find it, or of how a magnet was used to send a secret message?

Can you test different materials and write a list of which are attracted to the magnet and which are not?

Links with Maths

Can you time how long it takes your car to move a set distance on a flat surface and up a ramp, and calculate the difference between the two?

✓ Opportunities for learning

- Exploring magnetic forces and how they can be useful.
- Exploring how opposite magnetic poles attract and similar poles repel.
- Investigating which materials are attracted to magnets.

Super surfboard

> Oh no! You want to go surfing but there's no wind or waves today. How can you get a surfboard to move?

Here's what you will need

- Large lolly stick
- Container of water
- Washing up liquid
- Drinking straws of different sizes

Here's what you can do

1 Put about 3 cm of water in the container.

2 Place the lolly stick on the surface of the water.

3 Add a little washing up liquid at one end of the stick and watch the surfboard zoom off, away from the washing up liquid.

4 Now try to move your surfboard by blowing down a straw. Try thick and thin straws, short and long straws. Which work the best?

Questions to think and talk about

How far and how fast does the surfboard move?

If you keep adding washing up liquid, does the surfboard keep moving?

What weather conditions does a real surfer need to move fast over the water?

Which size and shape straws make moving the surfboard the easiest?

How much difference does it make to the surfboard if you blow harder?

Extra Activities

Can you make the lolly stick look more like a surfboard? Does it still move through the water as well as before?

Ask a friend to blow waves over the surface of the water with a straw. Does the surfboard still move when you add the washing up liquid?

Have a race with a friend. Who can get their surfboard to the finish line first?

Can you set up a track with several turns and move the surfboard around the track?

Links with English

Can you write a poem about the perfect weather for surfing?

A surfer has been attacked! Talk about what might have attacked the surfer and create a warning poster for the surfers' beach.

Links with Maths

Set up a race for yourself and a friend. Measure the distance of the race and time how long it takes your surfboard to reach the end by blowing it along using a straw. Who is the fastest?

✓ Opportunities for learning

- Investigating the forces needed to move the surfboard in different directions.

- Exploring the relationship between the force and the speed of movement.

- Using directional language for moving the surfboard around the water.

Can you cross the river?

 Can you build 3 boats using different materials to help the Gingerbread Man cross the river? Your boat must be able to carry a small load so he can build a bridge to get back to the other side.

Here's what you will need

- Lemons, oranges or limes, cut in half with the flesh removed
- Playdough
- Lolly sticks and cocktail sticks
- Cardboard
- Jam jar lids
- Sponges
- Egg cartons
- Corks
- Aluminium foil
- Water tray
- Small figures or objects

Here's what you can do

1 Build three boats using different materials each time. If you build three you can decide which one is best.

2 Place the boats in a filled water tray to see if they float. If they float, add small objects or figures to find out how well the boats float.

Science Spark

Questions to think and talk about

Do all the boats float? Which boat floats best?

Does it matter where in the boat you put the extra weight?

Does it make a difference if the water is deeper?

Which materials are the most waterproof?

What do you notice about materials that float? Do they have any properties in common?

Extra Activities

Does the shape of the boat affect how it floats?

Can you make the boats move across the water? How many different ways can you do this?

How else could the Gingerbread Man cross the river? Can you think of three more ideas?

Links with English

Can you write an alternative ending to the Gingerbread Man story where he builds a boat and escapes across the river?

How might the Gingerbread Man send a signal to ask for help? Who or what might come to his rescue?

Links with Maths

How much weight can you add before each boat sinks? What is the maximum weight a boat can hold?

How far does each boat travel if you blow it?

Opportunities for learning

- Understanding more about why some objects sink and some float.
- Understanding how different materials can be used to make a boat more buoyant.
- Using key vocabulary including sink, float, light, heavy, buoyancy, density.
- Calculating how much objects weigh.
- Comparing different solutions to a problem.

Helicopter heroes

 You need to rescue a friend from a mountain and only a helicopter can reach them. Can you build a model helicopter to get to them?

Here's what you will need

- Paper or card
- Sellotape
- Scissors
- Strong glue dots
- Paper clips
- Bluetack or modelling clay
- Small boxes
- Timer

Here's what you can do

1 Use the template below as a guide to help you make your helicopter.

2 Fold up the two outer strips and add a paper clip to fasten them together. You can use bluetack or modelling clay instead of a paper clip.

3 Throw the helicopter as high as you can and watch it spin to the ground.

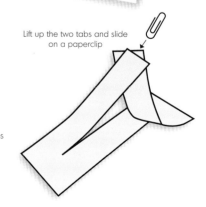

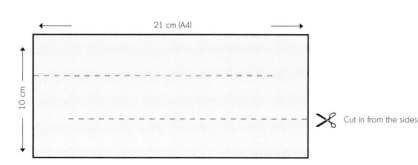

21 cm (A4)

10 cm

Cut in from the sides

Lift up the two tabs and slide on a paperclip

SCiENCE SPARk

Questions to think and talk about

Why does the helicopter fall to the ground?

Can you think of a seed that does the same thing as your helicopter? How do you think this helps the seed?

Can you find a way to make the helicopter fall more slowly?

Can you find a way to change the direction of spinning?

Links with English

Can you write a story about how your friend is rescued from the mountain?

What difficulties do you think a helicopter would encounter trying to land?

What would make a good landing spot?

Can you create a diary for a helicopter seed? What exciting adventures does it have?

Links with Maths

Create a bulls eye on the ground with different scoring areas and design a game where players score points depending on where the helicopter lands. How can you make the game fair?

How long do different helicopters take to fall from the same height? Try each three times and calculate the average time taken for each to reach the ground.

Extra Activities

Make a large and a small helicopter and see if this makes any difference. Does changing the length or width of the blades change how the helicopter falls?

Try adding extra weight to the helicopter and see if this makes any difference.

Can you add a small box to the bottom of the blades so it looks like a real helicopter? Which size of blades works best with the extra weight?

What happens if you change the design of the helicopter? Does it work if it is a different shape?

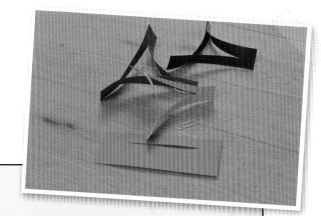

Opportunities for learning

- Understanding that objects fall to earth because of gravity.

- Understanding the effect of air resistance on the helicopter.

- Planning and carrying out a fair test investigation.

Race down the wall

You don't have much time and need to water several plants in one go. Can you build a water wall to direct water to three different places?

Here's what you will need

- Empty plastic bottles, different shapes
- Funnels
- Pipes and tubes
- Sellotape
- Watering can
- Cups or jugs
- Cable ties/staple gun/glue
- Containers for the water to flow into
- Fence or other vertical surface – make sure this is stable
- Timers
- Plants to water

Here's what you can do

1 Ask an adult to help cut the bottles into different sizes. The bottom needs to be completely cut off each one so water can flow all the way through.

2 Draw a plan of your water wall and make a list of all the materials you'll need. How will you direct the water to three different places?

3 Construct your water wall by attaching the containers and bottles using cable ties, a staple gun or glue. Place a plant under each pathway.

4 Use a watering can, bucket or other container to pour water down the water wall. Remember to place a container at the bottom to catch the water.

5 Use the timer to record how long a cup of water takes to flow down each path.

SCiENCE SPARk

Questions to think and talk about

Which is the shortest and longest route down the water wall?

How could you slow the flow of water?

How could you recycle the water flowing down the wall?

Can you improve your design?

Extra Activities

Can you choose bottles and containers so water moves along the three pathways at different speeds, or so the water flowing along each track reaches the bottom at the same time?

Can you use coloured water and build into your design an area where the colours mix? How many colours can you make?

Links with English

Imagine the water wall track is a water slide. Write a paragraph about how you think it would feel to slide down it.

Links with Maths

Time how long one cup of water takes to travel from the top to the bottom of each track. Can you design a table to record your results? If you use a sponge at the top, how long does it take for the water to completely drain from the sponge?

Can you change the track so the water travels twice as fast? Can you change the track so the water takes twice as long to reach the bottom?

✓ Opportunities for learning

- Designing and carrying out a simple investigation.

- Collecting and recording information.

- Working to an iterative design process.

Super shadows

 Make a shadow frame and see if a friend can guess what the shape is.

Here's what you will need

- Cardboard
- Decorative paper
- Contact paper
- Coloured transparent film (coloured plastic wallet folders work well)
- A sunny day!

Here's what you can do

1 Cut the cardboard into a frame shape and attach the contact paper to one side.

2 Use your decorative paper to cut out a shape.

3 Attach your shape to the sticky side of the contact paper.

4 Take your frame outside and see if you can make a shadow.

SCIENCE SPARK

Questions to think and talk about

Which type makes a good shadow?

What happens if you move the frame further from the ground?

Do you need a sunny day for your frame to work?

What else could you stick to the contact paper to make a shadow?

Extra Activities

Can you make a nature version of your frame using leaves and flowers?

Can you make a giant or mini frame?

Can you make a shadow using coloured transparent film?

Can you create a table, with at least 5 opaque, translucent and transparent items from around your house?

Links with English

Imagine that your house doesn't have any windows. What would it feel like inside? Can you think of 5 words to describe it?

Can you turn one of your shadow frames into a storyboard? What happens to your shadow character?

Links with Maths

How many opaque items can you find in one room?

Can you calculate what distance between the ground and your frame gives you the best shadow?

✓ Opportunities for learning

- Comparing and contrasting the suitability of different materials for making shadows.

- Considering why being opaque, translucent or transparent is a useful property.

- Understanding why and how shadows form.

- Understanding the relationship between the object, screen and shadow distance.

Can you stick it?

 You have been on a walk collecting lots of lovely natural items and you need to keep them safe. Will they stick to a sticky wall?

Here's what you will need

- Sticky back plastic
- Sticky tape
- Natural materials such as leaves, pinecones, sticks, feathers, flowers
- Weighing scales

Here's what you can do

1 Cut out a large piece of the sticky back plastic. This could be a square or a less obvious shape like a rocket, leaf or diamond.

2 Remove the back of the sticky back plastic to reveal the sticky side.

3 Use the thick tape to stick your sheet of sticky plastic onto a wall or fence, with the sticky side facing you.

4 Try to stick your leaves, sticks and feathers to the sticky wall.

5 Can you make a picture?

SCIENCE SPARk

Questions to think and talk about

Do all your natural items stick to the sticky wall? Which ones stick best?

What do you notice about the items that don't stick.

Can you weigh the items that don't stick and those that stick? Do you notice anything?

Extra Activities

Can you make a face, figure or a flower shape with your items?

Can you take your sticky picture off the fence or wall and use it to project shadows onto the ground?

Links with English

Create a leaf person on your sticky wall. Give him or her stick arms and legs and draw a face. Imagine the leaf person comes to life and escapes. Can you write a story about their adventure?

Links with Maths

Create a tally chart showing how many of each type of item you have collected. Can you sort your items by colour and size or make a pattern?

Can you use the scales to weigh each item and record the data in a table?

Try using a ruler to measure the length of your leaves, pinecones and flower petals.

✔ Opportunities for learning

- Measuring and recording data.
- Observing changes across seasons.
- Identifying common plants, nuts and seeds.
- Counting and sorting objects in different categories.

Messy colour lab

> You only have yellow, red and blue paint, but you would like more colours! Can you use the equipment in your laboratory to make at least three more colours?

Here's what you will need

- Small baking trays
- Water
- Red, yellow, blue, black and white paint
- Paintbrushes
- Different sized containers and measuring cylinders
- Pipettes
- Red, yellow and blue food colouring
- Paper towels

Here's what you can do

Painting on ice

1 Pour water into a baking tray and place in a freezer until frozen.

2 Use the ice as a surface to mix the paint colours together in different combinations. Can you make orange, green and purple?

3 Once you've finished, wipe the surface with a paper towel.

Colour mixing with water

1 Pour a small amounts of water into 3 containers and add a few drops of different food colouring to each.

2 Use a pipette to place a small amount of different colours of water into a clean container. What colour do you get? How many colours can you create?

Science Spark

Questions to think and talk about

How does it feel when you paint on the ice? Does it feel different as the ice melts?

How does the shade of the colour you made change depending on the amount of each primary colour used?

What happens if you added a little white or black paint or water to each colour?

Links with English

Can you write a set of instructions for how to make each colour?

Can you write a list of items that are red, yellow and blue?

Links with Maths

Count how many different colours you can make.

How many different shades of orange can you make? Can you order these from lightest to darkest?

Extra Activities

After painting on the ice, try placing a piece of paper on the ice and pressing down to transfer the paint onto the paper. Investigate using paper towels, writing paper, sugar paper, shiny paper and card. How much paint does each one absorb? Why do you think this is?

Use measuring cylinders to find the amount of water of each colour needed to make your favourite colour.

Add drops of coloured water into swirls of shaving foam. Do the colours mix?

Try adding a little bicarbonate of soda and vinegar to a measuring cylinder containing coloured water. What do you think will happen?

✓ Opportunities for learning

- Understanding that there are three primary colours which cannot be made from other colours.

- Measuring and recording capacity and volume.

- Sorting by category.

Sticky webs

 The spiders are having a problem making enough silk for their webs. Can you make a sticky web for a spider?

Here's what you will need

- Hula hoop
- Different types of sticky tape, such as sellotape, duct tape, masking tape
- Small pom-pom balls, bits of wool and other small, light objects

Here's what you can do

1 Attach different types of sticky tape to the hula hoop. Make sure the sticky side is facing towards you.

2 Gently throw different small objects at the spider web. Observe which ones stick to the web.

SCIENCE SPARK

Questions to think and talk about

Which objects stick best to the tape? How are these objects similar?

Which type of tape seem to be the stickiest?

Why do you think spiders have webs? How does it help them?

Links with English

Imagine you are a spider, waiting at your web for some prey to land.

Which insects do you hope you catch? Can you create a storyboard to describe what happens?

Links with Maths

How many different shapes can you find inside a spider web?

How many objects did you get to stick to your hula hoop web? What is the heaviest thing you can get to stick?

Extra Activities

Can you weave a spider web inside the rim of a paper plate?

Can you make a spider web shape with straws and plasticine?

Can you draw a food chain featuring a spider? What do you think will happen if there were no spiders?

✓ Opportunities for learning

- Understanding the properties of materials.
- Understanding the lifestyle of a spider and describing how spiders use their webs to obtain food.
- Understanding a spider's place in food chains.

Making Science Fun For Kids!

Bug hotels

 You would like to see more helpful insects in your garden. Can you find a way to attract them and help them stay safe over winter?

Here's what you will need

- Bamboo canes (ideal as they are hollow) or sticks
- Empty plastic bottle, clean empty tin or wooden box
- String
- Plant pot
- Leaves
- Flowers

Here's what you can do

1 Carefully cut the bamboo into small pieces so they fit inside your container. Ask an adult to help cut the bamboo.

2 Bundle the bamboo pieces together to they fit snugly inside your container. Tie up the bamboo pieces with some string.

3 Place the bundle of bamboo pieces inside the container. You could stuff the gaps with moss or dried grass too. Place the container outside.

4 Another idea is to fill a plant pot with leaves, turn it upside down and hang it somewhere on a piece of string. This creates a shelter many types of insects will love.

5 If you want to go large, fill a stack of pallets with pinecones, bricks, sticks, bamboo, stones and cardboard tubes. This will make a great habitat for a huge variety of insects.

Science Spark

Questions to think and talk about

Where would be a good place for the bug hotel? Think about the reasons why you want insects like bees and ladybirds in your garden.

Why do you think insects will like your bug hotel?

Why do you think your bug hotel will be especially useful to insects in winter?

Links with English

Can you write a story about an insect looking for a home? How does the insect feel when it finds your bug hotel?

Links with Maths

Can you keep a record of how many insects you spot in your bug hotel each week? Can you plot the data on a chart?

Extra Activities

Can you make a simple log pile home? These are perfect for beetles, frogs, hedgehogs and grass snakes.

Can you find more ways to attract helpful insects to your garden? Think about the type of flowers that bees like and where bees get their food.

Opportunities for learning

- Understanding that different insects like different environments, and that the materials used for the bug hotel are similar to the natural habitat of some insects.

- Understanding that some insects are pests but others are useful to have in a garden.

Minibeast maze

 Can you create a maze containing food for a spider, ladybird, slug, worm and caterpillar, and then use a magnet wand to move each minibeast to the correct food?

Here's what you will need

- Paper plate or thick sheet of cardboard
- Thick cardboard or small toy minibeasts
- Felt tip pens
- Small magnets
- Magnet wand
- Sticky tape
- Paperclip

Here's what you can do

1 First design a maze and make a list of what each minibeast likes to eat.

2 Draw your maze on a paper plate or piece of thick card, and then draw each food item at different points in the maze.

3 Draw each minibeast you want to feature on cardboard and cut it out. Attach a magnet or paperclip to the back of each of the minibeasts.

4 Place your magnetic minibeasts onto the maze and use a magnet wand to move each minibeast to the correct food.

Science Spark

Questions to think and talk about

How many minibeasts can you name?

Is it easy to move the minibeasts around using the magnet wand? Does it make any difference how you hold the magnet wand?

Which of your minibeasts are herbivores and which are carnivores?

Links with English

Imagine you're a worm, moving through the soil. What can you hear from the ground above? How do you think rain would feel on top of you?

Can you create a storyboard for 'A day in the life of a caterpillar'?

Links with Maths

Can you find out how long an earthworm usually is? Can you find out how big different types of minibeasts are?

Extra Activities

Can you add a drawing of a typical home for each of your minibeasts and use the magnet to guide each minibeast home?

Can you print out photographs of different minibeasts and sort them into groups depending on their characteristics?

Opportunities for learning

- Understanding that minibeasts can be very different.

- Appreciating that minibeasts live in habitats to which they are suited.

- Understanding that some materials are attracted to a magnet and others are not.

Easy life cycles

> You want to make a model of a butterfly life cycle, but all you have to make the model is a paper plate and some food items. Can you make a model butterfly life cycle with these?

Here's what you will need

A variety of food items, such as:

- Marshmallows or yoghurt raisins
- Sweet worms or spring onions
- Liquorice strips or long marshmallows
- Pasta bows or orange segments
- Paper plate
- Felt tip pens

Here's what you can do

1 Choose items of food that you think best fit each stage of the butterfly life cycle: Egg – caterpillar – chrysalis – butterfly.

2 Place your chosen items on a paper plate and draw arrows between each stage using felt tip pens.

3 Label each stage of the life cycle.

SCIENCE SPARK

Questions to think and talk about

How did you decide which edible item to use for each stage of the life cycle?

Why do you think butterflies are brightly coloured, but the chrysalis is usually brown or green?

Butterflies taste with their feet. Can you think of any reasons why this might be useful to them?

Links with English

Imagine you're a caterpillar. What does it feel like to spend most of the day munching on leaves? How do you think they taste? What is your favourite leaf?

You have just eaten through the chrysalis and emerged as a beautiful butterfly. Imagine how it feels as your wings grow stronger and you fly for the first time. What can you see?

Links with Maths

Butterfly wings are often symmetrical. Can you draw a beautiful, brightly coloured, symmetrical butterfly?

Can you find out how long butterflies spend in each stage of their life cycle?

Extra Activities

Can you write a sentence about each stage of the life cycle on the paper plate?

Caterpillars often shed their skin as they are growing. Can you add this stage into your model life cycle?

✓ Opportunities for learning

- Understanding the concept of a life cycle.

- Understanding that some animals go through dramatic changes (metamorphosis) in their life cycles.

- Understanding that living things live in habitats that meet their needs.

The astronaut's glove

 Oh no! You need to fix the airlock on the outside of the space station and your space suit glove has a rip in it. Can you fix it?

Here's what you will need

- Masking tape, duct tape and sellotape
- Cotton
- Plasters
- Waterproof glue
- Building blocks or bricks
- Thick latex glove with a rip in it
- Water
- Washing up bowl

Here's what you can do

1 Look at the materials you have available to fix the glove. Which do you think will work the best? See if you can work out a way to fix the rip in the glove. Remember the glove needs to be airtight.

2 Design and carry out three different tests to see if the glove is fixed. Here are some tests you could try:
  - Place your hand inside the glove and wiggle it around. Does the fix stay in place?
  - Try to build a tower using the blocks or bricks wearing the glove. Is it still fixed?
  - Fill the glove with water. Does it leak? If water can get out, so can air.

SCIENCE SPARk

Questions to think and talk about

Why does an astronaut need to wear a space suit to leave the space station?

What do you think is the best way to test whether the glove is airtight?

Do you think it's easy for astronauts to move outside the space station wearing their suits?

How could astronauts practice spacewalking while they are on Earth?

Links with English

Imagine you're an astronaut living in the space station. Can you write an e-mail to your family at home telling them about a typical day in space?

What do you think you would see from the space station? Can you write a paragraph describing the view and how it changes during the day?

Links with Maths

Can you find out how long it takes for the space station to make one orbit around Earth?

Try to build a tower with 10 blocks both with and without gloves. Can you compare how long it takes each time?

Extra Activities

Try to push pipe cleaners into the holes in a colander whilst wearing gloves; is it harder than just using your hands?

Look at the different fixing materials under a microscope. Do the waterproof and non-waterproof materials look different?

✓ Opportunities for learning

- Understanding that space is a hostile environment and how astronauts can survive in space.

- Considering how the properties of materials affect their suitability for a task.

- Understanding how to set up a simple test.

Landing pad

Your astronaut has blown off course and is about to crash land.
Can you build him or her a safe landing pad?

➤ Here's what you will need

- Hard boiled eggs for astronauts
  (water balloons could also be used)
- Sellotape
- Duct tape
- Scissors
- A variety of materials for constructing
  a landing site (cardboard boxes,
  plastic bottles, rubber bands, bubble
  wrap, bits of foam or polystyrene,
  old newspapers, etc.)
- Timers

Here's what you can do

1 Drop your egg astronaut from the same height onto different surfaces. Try surfaces
  like tarmac, grass, astroturf and bare soil. Does the shell crack on all the different
  surfaces?

2 Think about how you can use the materials to design a landing pad for your egg
  astronaut.

3 Make a landing pad, then put it on a hard surface where the egg will crack if
  dropped with no protection.

4 Hold the egg astronaut above your head and drop it onto the landing pad.

5 Does your landing pad save your egg astronaut?

Questions to think and talk about

Which materials are likely to make a good landing pad? Why do you think these materials will be good to use?

How big does your landing pad need to be?

Can you think of a good way to compare different landing pads?

Extra Activities

Try dropping your egg into water. How deep does the water need to be for the egg shell not to crack when you drop it in the water? Can you measure the size of the splash the egg astronaut makes?

Can you make a parachute for your egg astronaut to slow its descent?

Links with English

Imagine you are the egg astronaut. How does it feel to be hurtling towards Earth? Are you confident the landing pad will save you? What will you say in a final phone call to your family on Earth?

You need to give step by step instructions to a builder over a radio for how to build your landing pad. Create a radio conversation between you and the builder.

Links with Maths

Is it possible to time how long the egg takes to fall? How much more slowly does the egg fall if it has a parachute?

Try weighing all your egg astronauts. Do they weigh the same? Are the biggest eggs the heaviest eggs?

✓ Opportunities for learning

- Describing the properties of materials.
- Considering how the properties of materials affect their suitability for a task.
- Understand how to set up a simple test.

Space food

The astronauts would like to take apples with them into space, but they don't want the apple peel and cores. Can you find a way to keep apple slices fresh?

Here's what you will need

- Washed apples cut into slices
- Bananas cut into slices
- Salt
- White vinegar
- Water
- Lemon juice
- A fridge

Here's what you can do

1 Wash an apple, then slice it so you have plenty of slices.

2 Leave some slices in the air to see what happens. You can eat the rest!

3 After a while the slices don't look very appetising.

4 See if you can find a way to keep them fresh. You could try:
   - Putting them in water
   - Putting them in a fridge
   - Putting them in a freezer
   - Putting them in lemon juice
   - Putting them in white vinegar
   - Drying them over a radiator

   What else can you think of to try?

5 Look at the slices after 10 minutes, an hour and a day. Which slices look good to eat? Which slices still taste good?

6 Which was the best way to keep the apples fresh?

Science Spark

? Questions to think and talk about

How can you tell if food is spoiled or past its best? Does it matter if the apple goes brown if it still tastes good?

How do you keep your food fresh at home?

Salt is sometimes used to keep meat or fish fresh. Do you think salt would be good to use to keep apples fresh?

Links with English

Can you create a poster on how to keep food fresh?

Can you write a story about a week in the life of an apple?

Links with Maths

If you have two apples, how many pieces should you cut each apple into to give you 8 equal-sized pieces?

Can you time how long it takes for a slice of apple to go brown? Does this happen faster in a warm room?

Extra Activities

What happens if you use a banana instead of an apple?

Opportunities for learning

- Understanding that food spoils over time.
- Understanding simple methods of food preservation.
- Measuring and recording changes over time.

Solar system

Can you use fruit to create a model of our solar system?

Here's what you will need

- Different fruits, for example: melons, grapes, blueberries, apples, cherry tomatoes, oranges, limes, lemons, satsumas, pomegranates
- Cardboard and pens to create labels
- Rulers or tape measures

Here's what you can do

1 Arrange your fruit in order of size.

2 Find a fruit that most resembles each planet in our solar system. Think about the size and colour.

3 Place your fruity planets in order of how they orbit the Sun, and make a label for each.

Questions to think and talk about

Are some planets harder to match to a fruit than others?

Which is the biggest planet? Which is the smallest?

Which planet is nearest the Sun? Which is furthest away?

Extra Activities

Is it easier to make a solar system if you slice the fruit in half?

Can you add moons to your fruity solar system? You will need to do some research to discover which planets have moons and how many they have.

Can you find out something interesting about each of the planets?

Links with English

Imagine you're travelling around the solar system in a space ship. Can you write a postcard to a friend from each planet, telling the friend what the planet looks like and what it would be like if you could land there?

Links with Maths

Arrange your fruity planets in order of size. How will the order of planets change if you arrange them according to their distance from the Sun? How will the order change if you arrange them according to their distance from Earth?

Can you find out the average temperature on each planet and place them in order from highest to lowest temperature?

Can you weigh each fruity planet and record your results in a table?

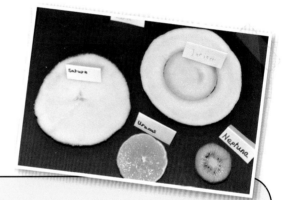

✓ Opportunities for learning

- Measuring and recording weight.
- Sequencing objects according to their characteristics.
- Researching information about the planets.

Icy rescue

 Oh no! You've found a superhero trapped in ice. How can you rescue him or her quickly?

Here's what you will need

- Small action superhero figure
- Small containers
- Salt
- A freezer
- Warm water
- Cold water
- Droppers or pipettes

Here's what you can do

1 Place your superhero figure into a container and fill it with water. Place the container in a freezer until the water is frozen.

2 How can you get the superhero out of the ice?

3 Use droppers to drop warm and cold water onto the ice. Which melts the ice fastest?

4 Try adding a little salt to the ice. What do you notice?

5 Try this again using three ice cubes made using the same amount of water. Add warm water to one, cold to another and salt to the last one. How long does each take to completely melt?

SCIENCE SPARK

Questions to think and talk about

Does warm or cold water melt the ice faster? Why do you think this is?

What happens when you add salt to your ice?

Do you think salty water would freeze in your freezer?

Why do you think we put salt and grit onto roads when the weather is cold?

Extra Activities

Try making ice cream by placing cream in one sealable sandwich bag and ice and salt in a second sandwich bag. Place the cream bag inside the ice and salt bag and squash them together until the cream freezes. This works really well if you add flavours such as vanilla or use flavoured milk.

Remember to wear gloves as the ice can get very cold.

Make a sheet of ice by freezing a thin layer of water in a tray. Try rolling a toy car over the sheet of ice, then sprinkle salt over the ice and try rolling the car again. The salt should start to melt the ice so that the car grips better to the ice sheet .

Links with English

How did the superhero become trapped in the ice? Can you create a storyboard to explain what happened?

Your superhero needs to go on a midnight rescue mission, but it's very dark and the roads are slippery because of ice. Can you create a list of items he/she should take to stay safe?

Links with Maths

Use a timer to time how long ice cubes or ice decorations take to melt. Can you record your results in a table or on a graph?

Use a measuring cylinder to accurately measure water so you have 3 ice cubes containing the same amount of water.

Opportunities for learning

- Measuring and recording time.

- Sequencing events in chronological order.

- Understanding that water changes state depending on its temperature.

- Understanding how to set up a simple test.

Superhero slime

 You have run out of superhero slime. Can you make some more?

Here's what you will need

- Cornflour
- Water
- Food colouring - optional
- Ice cube trays
- Mixing bowl
- Colander, funnel and beakers

Here's what you can do

1   Pour a small amount of cornflour into a mixing bowl. Add water slowly and mix it with the cornflour until it becomes thick and slimy.

2   Try squeezing the cornflour into a ball. It should feel quite hard. Open your hand and watch as the cornflour slime runs through your fingers.

3   Try pouring the slime through a colander. What happens?

Questions to think and talk about

Can you squeeze the slime into a ball? What does it feel like?

What do you think would happen if you added more water to your slime?

How could you make the slime thicker?

How do you think the slime will fall through the colander if you use less water?

Does the slime flow faster or more slowly than water?

Extra Activities

Pour some slime into an ice cube tray and place in a freezer until frozen. Remove from the tray when it is frozen, then leave the cubes in different places to discover where the slime cubes melt the fastest.

Can you predict which will melt first? Try comparing the time taken for a slime ice cube to melt with an ice cube made from just water.

Can you freeze a superhero in the slime? You could blindfold a friend and ask them to guess what you have hidden in the slime!

Links with English

Imagine you are stuck in the slime and need to be rescued by a superhero. How do you feel when you're stuck, and when you first see the superhero coming to rescue you?

Links with Maths

Can you use a stopwatch to time how long the slime ice cubes take to melt and record your results in a table or on a graph?

Try measuring the slime dropping from a colander. What is the longest slime strand you can make?

✓ Opportunities for learning

- Measuring and recording time.
- Sequencing events in chronological order.
- Understanding that cornflour slime doesn't behave like a standard liquid.
- Understanding how to set up a simple test.

Fly like a superhero

Your superhero has lost their flying power. Can you find a way to help him or her?

Here's what you will need

- Normal width drinking straws
- Wide drinking straws
- Cardboard
- Paper
- Scissors
- Glue/sellotape/double-sided tape
- Felt tip pens

Here's what you can do

1 Cut the wider straw so you have a piece about one third of the length of your normal width straw.

2 Completely seal one end of the wide straw with sellotape. Make sure no air can pass through it.

3 Draw a picture of your superhero on a piece of paper and use sellotape or glue to attach it to the wider straw.

4 Place the wider straw onto one end of the normal width straw and blow! Your superhero should fly through the air.

5 Try pointing the straw at different angles and blowing in different ways.

Science Spark

Questions to think and talk about

What happens if you blow very hard down the straw?

What happens if you point the straw straight upwards?

What do you think might happen if you use a longer straw?

Why do you think you need to cover the end of the wide straw with sellotape?

Links with English

Can you write a short story about how your superhero lost his or her flying power?

What do you think superheroes like to eat? Can you make a list of superhero foods and why your superhero likes to eat them?

Links with Maths

Can you measure how far your superhero flies when you change the angle of the straw as you blow? Record your results in a table or graph.

Which angle is the best for flying? What's the furthest your superhero can fly?

Extra Activities

Try flying your superhero outside on a windy day to see what happens.

Try making a squeezy bottle rocket using a similar method to the straw rocket. Bottles with a sports top work well. You will need to seal around the thinner straw and bottle opening – e.g. using modelling clay.

Can you make a catapult to help your superhero fly?

✓ Opportunities for learning

- Measuring and recording time and distance.
- Understanding how to set up a simple test.
- Starting to think about forces, including air resistance and gravity.

Save the superhero

 The superhero's space ship is about to crash in the sea. Can you help him or her float, using only the materials on the space ship?

Here's what you will need

- Superhero figure - make sure this sinks
- Masking tape, sellotape and gaffer tape
- Pool noodle cut into segments
- Bubble wrap
- Washing up bowl
- Plasticine/modelling clay
- Small sponges
- Aluminium foil
- Bits of polystyrene packaging and/or foam
- Scissors

Here's what you can do

1 Look at the materials that are available and build something that you think will help your superhero to float. Fill the washing up bowl with water and test to see if it helps your superhero to float.

2 Draw and label a diagram of the flotation support you made.

3 Can you think of any improvements you could make to your design?

SCIENCE SPARK

Questions to think and talk about

What tests can you do to decide which materials to use?

What properties should your material have? Do materials that float have any similar properties?

How can you test your flotation support? Do you think it would work for two superheroes or a very heavy superhero?

What do children wear to help them float when they are learning to swim?

Extra Activities

What is the smallest amount of material you can use to make your superhero float?

Can you build a lifeboat that can rescue several people?

Can you find a way to make a lemon sink?

Links with English

Can you write a short story about how your superhero came down in the sea? Does someone come to rescue him or her?

Can you describe how your superhero will feel and what he or she can see when floating in the sea? Write a list of descriptive words that will be suitable to use.

Links with Maths

What is the maximum weight that your flotation support can hold up in the water?

If your superhero doesn't have any support, how long does it take him or her to reach the bottom of the bowl? What is the slowest you can make him or her sink?

Opportunities for learning

- Understanding that some materials float and other materials sink.
- Considering how the properties of materials affect their suitability for a task.
- Planning, constructing, testing and improving a design.
- Understanding how to set up a simple test.

Let's dance

 Which type of food is the best dancer?

Here's what you will need

- Plastic bowl
- Thin metal baking sheet
- Cling film
- Tape or elastic bands
- Drum and drum stick
- Rice
- Mini marshmallows
- Popcorn

Here's what you can do

1 Stretch the cling film over the top of the bowl and secure with tape or an elastic band.

2 Sprinkle a handful of rice over the cling film.

3 Hold the drum close to the bowl and beat it hard. What happens to the rice?

4 Investigate how the jumping of the rice changes depending on how hard you hit the drum.

5 Repeat the investigation using popcorn and mini marshmallows. Do they jump too? Which jumps the best?

SCIENCE SPARK

Questions to think and talk about

What do you think would happen if you move the drum further away from the rice bowl?

Do you think a balloon stretched over the bowl will work as well as the cling film? How about kitchen foil?

What do you think will happen if you make a quiet noise with the drum?

Links with English

Can you write a list of other items you think might jump up when you beat the drum? How about salt?

Links with Maths

Can you measure how high the rice jumps?

How far can you move the drum from the bowl and still get the rice to jump?

Extra Activities

What happens if you use different musical instruments rather than a drum? Can you still get the rice to jump?

Pour some rice onto a thin baking tray and place it on top of a subwoofer speaker. Hold the tray in place and start the music. What do you see?

✓ Opportunities for learning

- Understanding how sounds are made and associating them with something vibrating.

- Understanding that different sounds can be made using the same materials.

- Thinking about the effect of sound on materials.

Rock guitarist!

> Your guitar has broken and you need to play in a concert! Can you make a new guitar?

Here's what you will need

- Clean, empty, tin can with no sharp edges
- Variety of plastic and cardboard containers
- Elastic bands – different sizes and widths
- Cotton wool
- Water

Here's what you can do

1 Place an elastic band around your thumb and forefinger on one hand. Pluck the elastic band. What does it sound like?

2 Place the elastic band over one of your containers, then pluck it again. What does it sound like now?

3 Place the same elastic band over all your different containers and listen carefully to the sound it makes.

4 Choose a thicker elastic band and try it on each container again. Is the sound different from the first elastic band?

5 Fill each container half full with cotton wool and pluck the elastic bands again. What do you notice?

6 Fill each container with water, then pluck the elastic bands again. Does the sound change?

SCiENCE SPArk

Questions to think and talk about

Is the sound from the elastic band louder over a container than on your fingers?

How does the thickness of an elastic band change the sound produced?

Does the sound from the elastic bands change when you use different containers? Why do you think this is?

Why do you think adding cotton wool or water to the containers changes the sound produced?

Extra Activities

Find a way to make a louder sound. Find a way to make a quieter sound. Find a way to make a lower-pitched sound. Find a way to make a higher-pitched sound.

Can you make a string telephone by tying a piece of string between two tin cans (be careful of sharp edges)? Investigate how well you can hear a person speaking down the telephone when the string is loose and when pulled tightly. Try using different thickness of string and different materials for the speaker and receiver (for example paper cups, yoghurt pots and polystyrene cups).

Links with English

Can you write a short song and play your guitar as you sing?

Links with Maths

How many different sounds can you make with one guitar?

Try different lengths of string for a tin can telephone. Which length allows you to hear the other person most clearly?

✓ Opportunities for learning

- Understanding how sounds are made and associating them with something vibrating.

- Understanding that different sounds can be made using the same materials.

- Thinking about how sound can be muffled.

- Understanding that sounds vary in pitch and that the pitch depends on the size of the vibrating object.

Scoop a sound

 Can you make some instruments for a band using different noisy items?

Here's what you will need

- Buttons, small jingle bells, dried beans, marbles, paper clips, small pom poms, cotton wool balls, beads, etc
- Plastic spoons or scoops
- Metal spoons
- Wooden spoons
- Clean, empty tin cans
- Plastic containers – ideally some similar and some different sizes
- Elastic bands
- Balloons with the end cut off

Here's what you can do

1 Put different materials for making sounds into plastic containers. You can use scoops or spoons to add different combinations of the sound materials. The containers should be about one third full.

2 Stir each container with the plastic, metal and wooden spoon. Listen to the sound each one makes.

3 Now try this with the tin cans and see if the sound is still the same.

4 Stretch a balloon skin over each plastic container or tin can and secure with an elastic band or tape.

5 Try shaking each container and tin can and listen to the sounds they make.

SCiENCE SPARk

Questions to think and talk about

Can you tell what is inside the can by the noise it makes?

Is the sound different if you bang the drum skin compared to when you shake the tin can or plastic container?

Why do you think some of the objects don't make much sound?

Links with English

How many different words can you think of to describe the sounds you can hear? How about ping, jingle, clink?

Can you match sounds with different materials? Do all metals make a clanging or ringing type noise? How would you make a scratching sound instead of a scraping sound?

Links with Maths

Pick your favourite-sounding tin can and weigh the contents, separating out each different type of object you've used. Can you place them in order of most to least used?

Extra Activities

Instead of placing a balloon skin over the top of your containers, use elastic bands to make a guitar. How can you change the sound it makes when you pluck the elastic band? Does the sound made when you pluck the elastic band change depending on the contents of the tin can?

Compare the sounds you get when you beat different-sized tin cans with a wooden spoon.

☑ Opportunities for learning

- Understanding how sounds are made and associating them with something vibrating.

- Understanding that different materials can make different sounds depending on their properties.

- Thinking about how sound can be muffled.

- Understanding that sounds vary in pitch and that the pitch depends on the size of the vibrating object.

- Thinking about using words to describe sounds.

Vibrations, vibrations

> Discover how the length of an object affects the sound it produces as it vibrates in this easy activity.

Here's what you will need

- Craft sticks
- Plastic ruler
- Wooden ruler
- Sticky tape

Here's what you can do

1 Place a craft stick on the edge of a table so one half is on the table and one half off the table.

2 Hold the craft stick in position by placing one finger on the end of the craft stick on the table. Now push down on the other end of the craft stick then let go, using a finger on your other hand. Listen to the sound that it makes.

3 Now repeat this using two fingers on the half of the craft stick on the table. How is the sound different?

4 Investigate the different sounds you can make by changing how much of the craft stick is on the table, how much pressure you apply to the stick and how hard you push the stick down.

5 Repeat this using a plastic ruler and a wooden ruler instead of the craft stick. Does the sound change?

SCIENCE SPARK

Questions to think and talk about

How fast does the craft stick vibrate if more of it is off the table? If more of it is on the table?

Can you count how long it takes for the craft stick or ruler to stop vibrating?

How can you make a higher-pitched sound?

How can you make a louder sound?

Links with English

Stand outside and make a note of all the sounds you can hear. Where do you think the furthest-away sound is?

Can you write a sentence about each sound you can hear?

Links with Maths

Can you play a simple tune, using several rulers at different positions on the table? Using just one ruler, can you write a tune by specifying how much of the ruler should be off the table when is it pushed down?

Can you count how many sounds you can hear inside and how many outside? Where can you hear the most sounds? How many sounds can you hear if you cover your ears?

Extra Activities

Can you use sticky tape to attach several rulers to a table, arranging them so each makes a different sound?

What happens if you attach a small bell to the end of each ruler?

✓ Opportunities for learning

- Understanding how sounds are made and associating them with something vibrating.

- Understanding that different materials can make different sounds depending on their properties.

- Understanding that sounds vary in pitch and that the pitch depends on the size of the vibrating object.

- Finding patterns between the volume of a sound and the strength of the vibrations that produced it.

5 easy ideas to brighten up a sand tray

1 **Plastic bugs**

The sand tray could be used for:

- Sorting bugs in different ways, e.g. by colour, number of legs, segmented or non-segmented bodies, what they eat, etc. Draw circles in the sand and use plastic tweezers to move the bugs to the correct sorting circle.

- Making habitats for bugs. What kind of habitats do bugs like to live in?

2 **Sand drawing**

Use a rolling pin to make a flat surface on the sand, then draw, write or make patterns using items in the tray. Good items to use include sticks, paintbrushes and feathers. A large comb is a great addition to this tray.

3 **Make a ramp or rollercoaster**

Add some strips of wood or thick cardboard to use as ramps. Try racing toy cars down them, testing how far the car travels across the sand with the ramp at different angles.

Or use scoops, pipes and cardboard tubes to make a rollercoaster in the sand tray.

4 **Sand patterns**

Use colanders and sieves to make patterns with dry sand. What kind of patterns can be made? Does wet sand make the same patterns?

5 **Making footprints**

Use a rolling pin to make a flat surface on the sand, then add toy dinosaurs and make footprints in the sand. Spray some water onto the sand surface and investigate whether dinosaurs make better footprints in wet or dry sand.

SCIENCE SPARK

5 easy ideas to brighten up a water tray

1 Washing line

Construct a washing line over the top of the water tray. Cut different materials into clothing shapes and hang them on the washing line. Dip each material fully in the water and investigate how long they take to stop dripping water.

2 Icy Arctic

Add small ice cubes with characters or letters frozen inside, as well as plastic Arctic animals (e.g. polar bears, seals) for a wintry experience. Notice how much of the ice cube sits above the water and try blowing the ice cubes around with straws in the chilly Arctic wind. See how long the ice cubes take to melt when they are in the water.

3 Water slides

Use sections of plastic gutter or pipe to create a water slide for small characters. Use a timer to record how long it takes for the characters to slide down different length or different gradients. Do they slide faster if you use more water?

4 How much water?

Place different sizes of plastic syringes, pipettes, measuring cylinders and beakers into the tray. Use the syringes or pipettes to fill up the beakers and measuring cylinders. Notice how much water you suck up into the syringe or pipette each time. Use dice to roll a number and try to fill up a syringe with the same amount in ml, or squirt the same amount in ml from a pipette.

5 Washing station

Add toy animals and cars to the water tray and wash them using toothbrushes and small sponges. Try leaving them to dry in different areas of the garden or playground to see where they dry first.

5 easy science writing prompts

1 **How does your garden grow?**

Role: Expert gardener at a big garden centre
Audience: New team member

Task: Write a set of instructions explaining to your new team member what plants need to grow and stay healthy. This could be developed further into a Do's and Don't's poster for the staff at the garden centre.

2 **At the zoo**

Role: Zoologist
Audience: School children coming to visit on a trip

Task: Create a sorting challenge for visiting children to sort the zoo animals into carnivores, herbivores and omnivores. This could be developed further by choosing an animal and creating an information board for that animal.

3 **What's the weather like?**

Role: Weather forecaster
Audience: People reading a newspaper

Task: Find a pictorial weather forecast for the next few days and write this as a newspaper weather forecast. This could be developed further by writing a weather forecast for each season using typical weather patterns found at each time of year. Remember to mention the length of the day at that time of year too.

.4 **Make it!**

Role: Child at a school
Audience: Caretaker

Task: Create a list of materials that would make a good desk and materials that wouldn't.. Think about the properties a desk needs. This could be developed further by writing a letter asking the caretaker to build a new desk for your classroom, suggesting materials that might work well. Do you need any extra features? Maybe a penholder?

5 **Eating healthily**

Role: A teacher concerned about children not eating enough healthy foods
Audience: The children in your class

Task: Create a poster explaining to your children why they should eat healthy foods, with examples of what to eat and what to avoid. This could be developed further by writing about enjoyable ways to exercise.

ScïENCE SPARk

More prompts for imaginative writing

1 **You are a beautiful butterfly.**
   How does it feel to fly around a garden full of flowers? Which flowers do you like to land on? Do you know their names?

2 **Imagine you are in a forest.**
   What natural materials can you find to make things with? What will you make?

3 **What can you find out about star constellations?**
   Can you make up a story about your favourite constellation?

4 **Imagine you are an earthworm and it starts to rain.**
   Rain means you won't dry out so you can explore more easily above ground. Where will you go? What will you find?

5 **What do you think would be the perfect human habitat?**
   Write about what it looks, feels and smells like. Who or what is there with you?

Why does it happen? – the science behind the activities

Incy Wincy spider

Waterproof materials do not let water through and do not soak up water.

Absorbent materials soak up water and let water pass through them.

The cow jumped over the Moon

When you push down on the milk bottle top, the lolly stick catapult arm bends, giving it energy. When the arm is released the energy is released and transferred to the ping pong ball which flies through the air.

The further down the lolly stick is pushed the more force is needed, which gives the lolly stick more energy to transfer to the ping pong ball, making it travel further.

Helping Jack and Jill

You can exert more force by pulling a rope downwards than by lifting the bucket upwards. You are able to use the weight of your body to help you.

Passing the string over a roller helps to reduce friction.

A rope and pulley system is more complicated than a roller. It is made from two or more wheels with a rope looped over them, and at least one of the wheels isn't fixed in position.

A secret message for Hansel and Gretel

Lemon and lime juice are very difficult to see on white paper, but when heated they turn brown, revealing the message.

The white crayon also can't be seen on white paper, but its waxy surface means that if you colour or paint over the top you can see it, as the crayon stays white but the paper around it becomes coloured.

Cress monster!

Cress seeds have everything they need to grow in the seed, which is why they can grow without nutrients from the soil.

The seeds need only need water to germinate (sprout from the seed), not sunlight, so they should still grow in the dark. However they cannot make the green pigment that makes leaves green so they will be yellow.

Great greenhouses

A mini-greenhouse provides plants with a warm, stable environment where they are protected from outside weather conditions.

Greenhouses allow you to start growing plants earlier than you can outside.

SCiENCE SPARk

Wonderful windmills

The force of the wind against the blades turns windmills around. Some areas have lots of windmills (wind turbines), including out at sea, and these are used to generate electricity. Wind power is a renewable energy source that doesn't pollute the environment, though we do need other ways to get electricity when the wind isn't blowing.

It's too loud!

Some materials allow sound to pass through them very easily and others absorb sound. Usually hard materials allow sound to pass through, while soft or fluffy materials absorb sound.

Moving with magnets

Magnets attract some objects but not others. Some metals (e.g. iron, steel) are attracted to magnets, but many other metals (e.g. copper, tin) are not.

Magnets have two poles. We call one the north pole and one the south. A north and south pole will attract each other while two north or two south poles will repel.

Super surfboard

Water molecules in a container form a 'skin' on the surface, which we call surface tension. When you add washing up liquid it disrupts the skin and lowers the surface tension, which makes the lolly stick move.

Helicopter heroes

The force of gravity pulls down on the paper helicopter. As it falls, air pushes up against each blade separately, making the helicopter spin.

Race down the wall

Water flows downwards because of a force called gravity. Gravity pulls everything down to the ground.

A water wall allows the flow of water to be controlled using different containers and tubes. The size of the exit point of the containers can be varied, as well as the slope/ gradient of the tubes, all of which affect the speed of the water flowing down the wall.

Super shadows

A shadow is formed when an object blocks light. To block light an object must be opaque (doesn't let any light through and not see-through) or translucent (a little bit see-through and lets some light through but not all of it). A transparent object will not make a shadow, as light passes through it.

Can you stick it?

Light objects should stick well to the sticky back plastic, but heavier items are more likely to fall off. Also objects without much surface area to stick, such as pinecones, are likely to fall off.

Messy colour lab

Red, blue and yellow are known as primary colours. They cannot be created by mixing other colours together.

Secondary colours are created when two primary colours are mixed together. These include orange, green and purple.

Bug hotels

Most insects like cool, damp conditions, so a good place to hang your bug hotel is in the shade. It's also a good idea to put it close to a natural environment for the insects you want to attract.

Bees prefer a sunny area, so nectar-rich flowers to attract bees should be grown in sunny places.

The astronaut's glove

A space suit creates an Earth-like environment inside the suit, allowing humans to walk around in space.

Space suits keep the body at the correct air pressure. They provide oxygen to breathe, remove carbon dioxide, protect against radiation and keep the astronaut warm.

Space food

Apples go brown because of an enzyme that reacts with the air when the apple is cut open. Acids such as lemon juice or vinegar prevent the enzyme from working properly, so the apple doesn't go brown.

Food starts to rot or decay mostly because of micro-organisms that break down the food. To slow the rate of food spoilage you need to slow the activity of the micro-organisms feeding on the food.

Micro-organisms grow and reproduce more slowly in cold temperatures, so fresh food stays in better condition in a fridge or freezer.

Food can also be preserved by being canned, smoked, salted, dried or pickled. These methods all slow the growth and activity of the micro-organisms which make them rot or decay, but they do change the taste of the food.

Icy rescue

Salt changes the freezing point of water, so water freezes at a lower temperature. This makes ice melt as it is no longer cold enough to freeze.

Superhero slime

Cornflour slime is also called oobleck. It is known as a non-Newtonian fluid as it doesn't flow like a normal liquid. If you make a ball with the slime it acts like it is a solid, but if you drop it on the floor it acts like a liquid again!

Fly like a superhero

When you blow air down the straw it travels to the end and pushes its way out, taking the superhero straw with it. The harder you blow into the straw the more energy the air has, and the further your superhero will fly!

Save the superhero

Although the flotation support makes the superhero figure weigh a little more, it also has a much bigger volume. This makes it displace more water, which makes the figure more buoyant.

The pockets of air in materials such as bubble wrap mean that the figure and bubble wrap together are less dense than the water, making the figure float.

Let's dance

The cling film stretched over the bowl is similar to your ear drum. Sound vibrations from the drum travel through the air to the cling film making it vibrate, and this makes the rice jump.

Rock guitarist!

Sounds are made when an object vibrates, and these vibrations make the air around an object vibrate. When the air vibrations reach the ear they shake tiny hairs that are connected to nerves. It is these nerves that send a message to the brain telling it that a noise has been heard.

When you pluck an elastic band over a container, the vibrations bounce off the surface of the container. This makes them sound louder.

Filling the container with a material like cotton wool means that some of the sound is absorbed, and this makes the elastic band sound much quieter.

Scoop a sound

The sound an object makes depends on the material it is made from. For example, metals are hard so they vibrate well and make a ringing noise. Cotton wool balls are soft and don't vibrate, so they don't make noise at all.

Vibrations vibrations

For a sound to be made, something must vibrate.

The piece of craft stick or ruler on the table can't vibrate, but the piece off the table can vibrate. Normally as the piece of craft stick or ruler off the table gets shorter, it vibrates faster. This produces a higher-pitched sound. When the piece off the table is longer, the vibrations are slower and the sound is lower-pitched.

SCIENCE SPARK